C000161421

100% NEW

DEVELOPING **LITER**

Photocopiable teaching resources for li

UNDERSTANDING AND RESPONDING TO TEXTS

Ages 5–6

Christine Moorcroft

A & C Black • London

Published 2008 by A & C Black Publishers Limited
38 Soho Square, London W1D 3HB
www.acblack.com

ISBN 978-0-7136-8460-5

Copyright text © Christine Moorcroft 2008
Copyright illustrations © Michael Evans 2008
Copyright cover illustration © Piers Baker 2008
Editor: Dodi Beardshaw
Designed by Susan McIntyre

The authors and publishers would like to thank Ray Barker and Rifat Siddiqui for
their advice in producing this series of books.

The authors and publishers are grateful for permission to reproduce the
following:

p.63: 'Seaside' © 1988 Shirley Hughes. From *Out and About* by Shirley
Hughes. Reproduced by permission of Walker Books Ltd, London. Every effort
has been made to trace copyright holders and to obtain their permission for
use of copyright material. The authors and publishers would be pleased to
rectify any error or omission in future editions.

A CIP catalogue record for this book is available from the
British Library.

Printed by Halstan Printing Group, Amersham, Buckinghamshire.

A&C Black uses paper produced with elemental chlorine-free pulp, harvested
from managed sustainable forests.

Contents

Recount

Using a dictionary

Information texts

Poetry

The senses

Pattern and rhyme

Themes

Introduction

100% New Developing Literacy Understanding and Responding to Texts is a series of seven photocopiable activity books for developing children's responses to different types of text and their understanding of the structure and purposes of different types of texts.

The books provide learning activities to support strands 7 and 8 of the literacy objectives of the Primary Framework for Literacy: Understanding and interpreting texts and Engaging with and responding to texts.

The structure of *100% New Developing Literacy Understanding and Responding to Texts: Ages 5–6* is designed to complement the objectives of the Primary Framework for Year 1 and to include the range of text types suggested in the planning for Year 1.

100% New Developing Literacy Understanding and Responding to Texts: Ages 5–6 addresses the following learning objectives from the Primary Framework for Literacy:

7 Understanding and interpreting texts

- Identifying the main events and characters in stories, and finding specific information in simple texts
- Using syntax and context when reading for meaning
- Making predictions showing an understanding of ideas, events and characters
- Recognising the main elements that shape different texts
- Exploring the effect of patterns of language and repeated words and phrases

8 Engaging with and responding to texts

- Selecting books for personal reading and giving reasons for choices
- Visualising and commenting on events, characters and ideas, making imaginative links to their own experiences
- Distinguishing fiction and non-fiction texts and the different purposes for reading them.

The structure of *100% New Developing Literacy Understanding and Responding to Texts: Ages 5–6* is designed to complement the structure of the Primary Framework for Year 1, which focuses on the following types of text:

- Narrative (stories with familiar settings, stories from a range of cultures, stories with predictable and patterned language, traditional and fairy tales, including plays, stories about fantasy settings)
- Non-fiction (labels, lists and captions, instructions, recount, dictionary, information texts, recount – fact and fiction)
- Poetry (using the senses, pattern and rhyme, poems on a theme).

The activities

Some of the activities can be carried out with the whole class, some are more suitable for small groups and others are for individual work. It is important that the children have opportunities to listen to, repeat, learn, recite and join in stories and rhymes for enjoyment. Many of the activities can be adapted for use at different levels, to suit the differing levels of attainment of the children (see the Teachers' notes at the bottom of each page). Several can be used in different ways.

These activities focus on specific aspects of reading and it is assumed that all teachers will also encourage children to choose their own books to read and to read them independently. The books represented in some of the activities have been selected to inspire the children's interest in them.

Reading

Most children will be able to carry out the activities independently but they will probably need help in reading some of the instructions on the sheets. It is expected that that someone will read them to or with them since children learn to recognise the purpose of instructions before they can read them.

Organisation

The activities require very few resources besides pencils, crayons, scissors and glue. Other materials are specified in the Teachers' notes on the pages: for example, fiction, poetry or information books.

Extension activities

Most of the activity sheets end with a challenge (*Now try this!*) which reinforces and extends the children's learning. These more challenging activities might be appropriate for only a few children; it is not expected that the whole class should complete them, although many more children might benefit from them with  appropriate assistance – possibly as a guided or shared activity. On some pages there is space for the children to complete the extension activities, but others will require a notebook or a separate sheet of paper.

Notes on the activities

The notes below expand upon those which are provided at the bottom of most activity pages. They give ideas and suggestions for making the most of the activity sheet, including suggestions for the whole-class introduction, the plenary session or for follow-up work using an adapted version of the activity sheet. To help teachers to select appropriate learning experiences for their pupils, the activities are grouped into sections within each book but the pages need not be presented in the order in which they appear, unless otherwise stated.

Stories and poems featured or suggested in this book and supplementary texts

Traditional tales
Chicken Licken, Hansel and Gretel, The Princess and the Pea, Little Red Riding Hood, The Gingerbread Man, Cinderella, The Sleeping Beauty, Goldilocks, The Wizard of Oz (all Ladybird)

Stories from different cultures
The Classic Tales of Brer Rabbit (Joel Chandler Harris, Running Press)

Stories in fantasy settings
Cloud Land (John Burningham, Red Fox), *The Magic Bed* (John Burningham, Cape), *Falling Angels* (C Thompson, Hutchinson), *The Dream Keeper* (Roger Inkpen, Dragonsworld), *Metal Mutz* (David Ellwand, Templar), *William and the Night Train* (Mij Kelly, Hodder), *Phoebe and the Monster Maze* (Caroline Castle, Hutchinson), *Rainbow Fish* (Marcus Pfister, North South), *Rainbow Fish to the Rescue* (Marcus Pfister, North South), *Where the Wild Things Are* (Maurice Sendak, Harper Collins), *The Kiss that Missed* (David Melling, Hodder)

Useful books of poems and rhymes
The Oxford Nursery Rhyme Book (Iona & Peter Opie, Oxford), *The Oxford Nursery Book* (selected by Ian Beck, Oxford), *Poems for the Very Young* (selected by Michael Rosen, Kingfisher), *The Puffin Book of Fantastic First Poems* (edited by June Crebbin, Puffin), *Finger Rhymes* (selected by John Foster, Oxford), *Out and About* (Shirley Hughes, Walker), *The Hutchinson Treasury of Children's Poetry* (edited by Alison Sage, Hutchinson)

Useful websites
Stories from other cultures
http://www.otmfan.com/html/brertar.htm, http://www.ongoing-tales.com/SERIALS/oldtime/FAIRYTALES/tarbaby.html (the story of Brer Rabbit and the Tar Baby in the original dialect)
http://www.americanfolklore.net/folktales/ga2.html (Uncle Remus stories in the original dialect)
http://homepage.ntlworld.com/matt_kane/uncle%20remus%20tales.htm#An%20Uncle%20Remus%20Tale (modern translation)
http://www.bbc.co.uk/cbeebies/tikkabilla/stories/bbm.shtml (The Rupee Tree and other tales)

Dual-language books
http://www.kingston.gov.uk/browse/leisure/libraries/childrens_library_service/dual_language.htm

Selected fiction and non-fiction books and book boxes
http://www.badger-publishing.co.uk/,
http://www.madeleinelindley.com/aboutus.aspx

Fairytales
http://www.bbc.co.uk/cbeebies/storycircle/fairystories/,
http://fairy-tales.classic-literature.co.uk/ (online text),
http://www.teachernet.gov.uk/teachingandlearning/library/fairytales/ (using fairytales in the classroom)

This book is split into three main sections: **Fiction**, **Non-fiction** and **Poetry**. These are subdivided to match the Planning Units of the Primary Framework for Literacy.

Fiction
Stories in familiar settings

The activities in this section are about stories set in familiar places, such as the home, garden, shops or the seaside. The children learn about story settings and how to identify the main events in a story. They also learn about the main characters in stories and have practice in re-telling stories in the correct sequence, drawing on the language patterns such as repeated catchphrases.

Sorting settings (page 13) is about story settings. The children learn the meaning of *setting* and identify the familiar settings of some stories. You could also provide a selection of books from the class library and ask the children to find stories set in specific places: home, garden, shops, school, park, seaside and so on. The children could sort the books as a group activity, with one child collecting books from each setting and the others co-operating by giving one another the books they are looking for. This could be linked with work in geography on the local area.

Lost on the beach (page 14) presents a story about a familiar experience in a familiar setting. It provides an opportunity for the children to visualise and comment on events and characters, making imaginative links to their own experiences. The children learn to identify the main events of a story and to consider the order in which they happen. There are opportunities for them to make links between the story events and their own experiences. This activity also consolidates the children's learning about story openings. The children could also talk about their own visits to the beach or about a time when they got lost, even if it was just for a short while. Ask them what it felt like, what they did and how they were found. This could be linked with work in citizenship on people who help us (people it is safe to approach if they get lost). You could also read with them the story *Lost* (Anthony Kerrins, Picture Puffins).

Jan and Gran (page 15) encourages the children to use syntax and context when reading for meaning. It also develops their understanding of story characters and invites them to comment on them. It provides an opportunity for them to visualise and comment on events and characters, making imaginative links to their own experiences. They say what they can find out about the story on page 14 about Jan and Gran. During the plenary session ask them how they know.

What Ali can do and **What can Ali do?** (pages 16–17) are about familiar experiences in a familiar setting. The children read the story about Ali on page 16 and then, using the list formats on page 17, list the things he can do. They could also make lists about characters in books they read: for example, listing the things a character likes, dislikes, can do, cannot do, wants, and so on. Lists could be made on an electronic whiteboard, with the children adding items as they remember them.

Stories from different cultures and stories with predictable and patterned language

These activities introduce some traditional stories from African and Indian folklore and provide a traditional British story containing predictable and patterned language, along with stick puppets to help the children to enact it.

Brer Rabbit and the Tar Baby (page 18) introduces a story from African folklore. *Brer Rabbit and the Tar Baby* is from the stories narrated by the fictional character Uncle Remus, a former slave, written by Joel Chandler Harris. Brer Rabbit is the enemy of Brer Fox, who is constantly trying to find ways to trap or trick him. You could also read the story in the original dialect (see page 5 for a list of websites). The children could compare the events in the story with those in other stories, especially those in which one character plays a trick on another.

The Rupee Tree: 1 and **2** (pages 19–20) introduces a traditional story from Indian folklore which the children are encouraged to enact. Explain that a Brahmin is a priest and that rupees are the money used in India. If possible, show the children some Indian currency. Discuss why the Brahmin would not accept money which had not been earned. Link this with the children's experiences of money and the value of money they have had to work for compared to any they have been given.

During the plenary session you could ask the children about what this story teaches people about money.

Chicken Licken and **Chicken Licken stick puppets: 1**, **2** and **3** (pages 20–24) present a well-known traditional tale containing predictable and patterned language, which the children are encouraged to join in as they enact the story using stick puppets. To make a stick puppet, the children should copy the completed page 21 on to card or glue a paper copy on to card. Cut up pages 22–24 so that each child in a group of four has a puppet. They make predictions, showing understanding of ideas, events and characters and have opportunities to enjoy the effects of the pattern of language and repeated words and phrases. Read the story aloud with the children joining in and supplying the missing words. Ask how they knew what was missing. They could first identify the characters and say what they did and what happened to them. Then they could predict, from the stick puppets, whom Chicken Licken meets and what he and they will say. You could also link this with work in poetry on rhyme: note the rhyming names of the characters and encourage the children to make up rhyming names for other animals (for example, *Horsey Lorsey*, *Doggy Loggy*, *Piggy Wiggy*, *Goaty Loaty*).

Traditional and fairy stories

These activities encourage the children to talk about traditional stories and fairytales they know and to read some less well-known ones. They identify the beginnings and endings of stories and look at particular characters and identify information in the text: for example, their appearance, behaviour and how they speak.

Tell me why (page 25) focuses on identifying and explaining events in stories the children are likely to know. It can be linked with sentence-level work on questions. The children learn about features of stories: beginnings, story language and typical characters. The children are required to think about the events and characters in fairytales and to say why the events took place. It is useful to discuss the behaviour and personal traits of characters such as the wolf and the bad fairy: ask the children if they are good or bad characters.

Hansel and Gretel trail (pages 26) encourages the children to re-tell the story of *Hansel and Gretel*. It helps them to follow the outline of the plot and to talk about the characters. The boxes in the trail provide clues about events in the story and act as prompts for re-telling it. Those

containing pictures of the characters help the children to focus on characters' behaviour. You could also make a display-sized trail of another traditional story or fairytale with the children contributing pictures and words. Link it with work in geography on direction: the children could set trails for others to follow.

The Princess and the Pea (page 27) develops the children's understanding of typical fairytale characters and events (princes looking for princesses to marry). They are required to show an understanding of events and characters. They could discuss what they have learned about real princesses in stories (their skin is much tenderer than that of ordinary people). They might also be able to think up other characteristics for real princesses: super hearing, tiny feet (like Cinderella) and so on.

Who will help Goldilocks? (page 28) features story characters. The children consider what they know about characters from their actions in stories. Ask them who is good and who is bad, and how they know. Also discuss which characters are likely to be kind to Goldilocks and what the bad characters might do to her. Continue this into a writing lesson in which the children tell or write their own stories based on what a character does when he or she finds Goldilocks lost in the woods.

Fantasy worlds

The activities in this section are based on fantasy settings of stories. The children visualise the settings, talk about how they differ from real-life settings and talk about what is new or unexpected. There are opportunities for them to predict what characters will do in these settings and to invent their own details.

Fairyland (page 29) presents a fantasy story setting in which characters from different fairytales meet. The children identify these characters and write their names. They could also predict how they might behave in this fantasy setting, especially when they meet one another. Ask the children which characters they think will be friends and which ones might harm others. Also discuss how this is different from a real-life setting. You could also read *Once Upon a Time* and *Once Upon a Picnic* by John Prater (Walker Books).

The Emerald City (page 30) is based on *The Wizard of Oz*. It focuses on the differences between the Emerald City and a real city and encourages the children to compare the two. Some children might be able to invent other details: for example, trees and other plants, pavements, roads and shops. This could be linked with work in geography on the local area. Other stories set in fantasy worlds are listed on page 5. You could also display pictures of real cities on an electronic whiteboard and help the children to change the colour of the pictures, making them green.

A strange place (page 31) provides a format for the children to invent their own fantasy story setting. They could also predict how known story characters or their own invented characters might behave there. The focus is on the difference between real and fantasy settings. During the plenary session invite volunteers to tell the others about their fantasy story setting. The others might be able to contribute ideas as to who might live there and what might happen there.

What did they want? (page 32) is about the characters in the fantasy world of *The Wizard of Oz*. After reading the story with the children, discuss what Dorothy, the Tin Man, the Scarecrow and the Lion want, and why. It will be useful to explain the meaning of courage. Children who undertake the extension activity will also consider the character of the Wizard. Encourage them to say how they recognise each character: what he or she looks like and his or her most noticeable features. Ask them what is special about each character.

Non-fiction
Labels, lists and captions

This section focuses on the use of one-word captions or complete sentence captions, how labels and lists are written and how they are used.

Making a salad: lists and **Making a salad: ingredients** (pages 33–34) are about how to use lists. Point out that the lists of salad ingredients are not written in sentences but as a list of single words. The children could also compose sentences about items which are required: for example, *I need a carrot*. This could be linked with work in design and technology on healthy eating. The children could draw and label pictures of the ingredients they plan to use and then write a list.

Victorian seaside search

(page 35) develops the children's ability to use pictures with captions in order to find specific information. Link this with work in history on the seaside: provide real items or photographs to enable the children to match each item with its modern equivalent before they begin this page. Point out that the captions are not written as sentences. The children could write a sentence based on each caption: for example, *This is a parasol*.

Instructions

In these activities the children learn to recognise sentences which give instructions and to distinguish between these, captions and story sentences.

Signs (page 36) is about how signs can give instructions. The children could first read some of the signs around the school and say what they tell them and how they are useful. Draw out that the signs give information about how to use things in the classroom and that these signs are different from the labels on page 36: they are written as sentences. Also draw out that these are instructions.

Strawberry milkshake (page 37) focuses on instructions. The children learn that a recipe tells the reader how to make something. You could point out how this is different from a story, in which the sentences say what happened. Also discuss how the sentences are difference from captions, which say what something is. This could be used in connection with work in design and technology on healthy eating. When finished and checked they could glue them into a notebook or onto a piece of paper and perhaps use them as instructions to help them to make a strawberry milkshake during another lesson.

Instructions for robots (page 38) focuses on instructions for making things. The children learn to recognise instruction sentences. They also interpret the instructions and check whether they have been followed when a robot was drawn or made. They could also write instructions to tell a friend how to draw a robot.

Instructions machine (page 39) helps the children to recognise the difference between sentences which say what has happened or give information and those which give an instruction. The children learn to change sentences about what they have done while making something into an instruction for someone else to follow. This activity could be linked with work in design and technology or art in which the children describe what they have done or made and then write instructions about how to do or make it. Point out that instructions never begin with *I* or *we*.

Recount

These activities are about non-fiction recounts. They provide sentences in the first person which tell of real-life events, rather than stories which are made up. They are useful in helping the children to distinguish between fiction and non-fiction.

A day at the farm (page 40) presents a recount of a class day out at a farm, but in the wrong order, so that the children can re-order it and then read it to check for sense. Point out the difference between the opening sentence and story openings. This is about a real day (*On Monday*) rather than *Once upon a time* or *One day*.

Questions about the farm (page 41) develops the children's understanding that non-fiction texts can be used to find the answers to questions. Note that the answers are not written as sentences and during the plenary session you could ask the children to give each answer as a sentence: for example, *They went to a farm*, *It was Monday*.

Making things (page 42) develops the children's understanding that non-fiction texts can be used to find information. Draw out that the information is written in sentences. You could use a chart like the one on this page for helping the children to record what happened in other non-fiction recounts they read. Point out that this is a useful way of making notes without writing sentences.

Bed time (page 43) focuses on the need to write a recount in the correct order if it is to make sense. The children read the series of four sentences and then re-write them in the correct order. The sentences could be displayed on an electronic whiteboard so that the children can drag them into the correct order and read them to check this. After completing this activity they could write or key in four sentences about what they do in the morning. Invite them to read their sentences and to check that they are in the correct order.

Using a dictionary

The activities in this section develop the children's understanding of alphabetical order and how this is useful in helping to find words in a dictionary.

Picture dictionary: 1 and **2** (page 44–45) provide practice in using alphabetical order. The children should first have been shown a picture dictionary and have explored the way in which the words are listed. Some children might need additional practice: for example, putting sets of three alphabet blocks or plastic letters in order. The children could also cut out the pictures and words and glue them into personal dictionaries (use an exercise book in which each page is headed by a letter of the alphabet in order). They could add other words as they come across them in their reading.

Page by page (page 46) develops the children's understanding of, and ability to use, alphabetical order. During the plenary session you could ask them which fruit comes first alphabetically. Ask them if they can think of another fruit for any of the pages: for example, apricot, blackberry, blueberry, date, grapefruit, lemon, melon. During the plenary session you could challenge the children to be the first to find given words in simple picture dictionaries. Ask them if they would look near the end or the beginning for something beginning with A, B, X, Y or Z.

All in order (page 47) provides practice for the children in using their developing understanding of alphabetical order to put three consecutive names in order. Some children might benefit from putting the initial letters of the names in order (use alphabet blocks or plastic letters) and than matching the names to the letters.

Information texts

This section is about the difference between fiction and non-fiction and how to use non-fiction books to find the answers to questions.

Titles game (page 48) helps the children to recognise books which contain stories and those which contain factual information. The children should first have compared some fiction and non-fiction books and noticed that fiction books contain stories and non-fiction books contain information. Show them a selection of fiction and non-fiction books and asking them to separate them into their different types. Discuss the different types of title and how they can recognise a story title and a non-fiction title. Also show them other features of non-fiction books: contents page, index, glossary.

Book choice (page 49) is about choosing an information book to answer a question. Show the children some non-fiction books, read the titles with them and ask them what they expect to find inside them. After they have matched the titles on this page to the questions you could help the children to find a book in the classroom which would answer one of the questions. During the plenary session invite volunteers to explain how they knew which books would help.

The Big Cats

What we know (page 50) is about preparing to find information from non-fiction books. Help the children to write what they know about them: for example, in one box they could list objects made of metal; in another they could write words to describe them (for example, *cold, hard*); in another they could write about the sounds they make when tapped and in another they could write the names of some metals (for example, *tin, iron, steel*). This could be linked with work in science on materials: in another lesson the children could contribute to the writing of questions about what they want to know about metal things.

A closer look (page 51) focuses on choosing, from a limited selection of books, the one in which the answers to questions on a specific topic can be found. You could model how to choose a book: for example, *'This one is called* Homes in the Past *so it might tell me about how people did the washing, what their cookers and floors were like and how they kept their houses warm. I can check if it will help by looking at the contents page – yes – here's a page about washing.'* This could be used in connection with work in history on homes. Explain that the children in the pictures want to know the answers to their questions about homes in the past.

Finding out (page 52) develops the children's understanding that the answers to questions can be found in non-fiction books because these give facts. They learn how to locate the information they need. You will need to model how to use the contents page, index and chapter headings of a book (also the pictures and captions) to locate information, to find the answer to the first question.

Poetry
The senses

This section provides activities to help the children to enjoy rhymes and poems and respond to them by exploring the effects of language. The emphasis is on sensory experiences and how they are described in words.

Rain (page 53) encourages the children to explore the effects of language. It provides an opportunity for reading and responding to poems that capture sensory experiences, practising and reading a poem in unison, following the rhythm and keeping time. The children can imitate and invent actions while reading the poem ('wiggling' hands down to show the rain falling in the first three pictures, and then arms held over the head as if making a roof). Encourage them to move their arms and hands to represent the rain. They could also make up their own poems, substituting rain for another type of weather (for example, sunshine, snow, wind, hail) and adjusting the actions accordingly.

Mud (page 54) provides an opportunity for reading and responding to poems that capture sensory experiences, practising and reading a poem in unison, following the rhythm and keeping time. The children can actually feel the wet sand (or mud, if you prefer) while reading the poem, which encourages them to explore the effects of language. When reading the poem aloud, emphasise the *s* sounds in *slippy, sloppy, squelchy, slither* and *slide*. Ask the children which phonemes in the poem make a wet sound. You could also read with the children *The Slimy Book* by Babette Cole (Picture Puffins).

Treasure hunt (page 55) develops the children's appreciation of the effects of language as they read descriptive words and find objects these words could describe. They are also encouraged to think up words to describe what they see, feel and hear. They could also make up poems about an object they find, using the words provided and adding others of their own. The poem could be modelled on *Mud* (page 54).

Loud and quiet (page 56) develops the children's appreciation of the effects of language as they read descriptive words for actions. Ask them which actions are loud and which are quiet and draw attention to the sounds of the words which help to communicate these effects.

Pattern and rhyme

The activities in this section encourage the children to hear, read and respond to rhymes and to explore the different patterns created by the ways in which sounds, words and phrases are used and by the way in which the text is laid out. The children have opportunities to join in poems in different ways: reciting, enacting or even singing.

I threw a pie (page 57) consolidates the children's appreciation of rhyme as they complete the sentences with rhyming words. They could also make up their own rhyming sentences based on these. The following could be used as starting points: *I threw a plane, I threw a table, I threw a bell, I threw a bed.*

I spy characters and **I spy cards** (pages 58–59) focus on rhyming patterns. The children could take turns to read the words on a completed card. Some children might be able to make up rhymes for other characters, such as the Three Blind Mice, the Farmer's Wife, the Knave of Hearts, Old King Cole.

Skipping rhyme (page 60) focuses on the rhythm of skipping. The children could skip (with or without ropes) before the rhyme is introduced. The rhyme could then be read to them as they skip. The children could then repeat the first verse in time to their skipping and then gradually introduce the other verses.

Lines (page 61) introduces the effect of the layout of a poem on the page. The children develop an appreciation of how this changes the way in which they read the poem. They could practise reading each poem as continuous prose (as it is set out here) and as a poem set out in four lines.

Themes

Two themes are introduced in this section: food and the seaside. Food poems could be linked with work in design and technology on healthy eating and seaside poems could be linked with work in history on the seaside. The children are encouraged to explore the effects of the words in the poems and to notice rhyme patterns.

Bubbling porridge page 62) develops the children's understanding of rhythm created by the way in which a poem is set out, the words used and the rhyme pattern. They could also talk about other 'bubbling' foods: potatoes, carrots, soup and so on. Draw out that all these bubbling foods are hot. Help the children to memorise the poem two lines at a time.

Picture this: seaside poems and **Picture this: seaside pictures** (pages 63–64) develop the children's appreciation of the different images a poem can conjure up about the same type of place through the use of language. Focus on one poem per lesson. Ask the children to describe the picture they see in their minds when they read or listen to each poem: the setting (a sandy beach, a rocky beach, rock pools, sand dunes and so on), the sea (calm, splashing waves, ripples, roaring breakers, strong pulling/sucking waves), objects and creatures (seaweed, crabs, shells, buckets, spades), actions (lively, fast, slow, gentle, strong). Ask them if the poem is about a real or imaginary seaside and how they can tell. As well as matching the poems to the pictures on page 64, the children could paint their own picture inspired by one of the poems.

Using the CD-ROM

The PC CD-ROM included with this book contains an easy-to-use software program that allows you to print out pages from the book, to view them (e.g. on an interactive whiteboard) or to customise the activities to suit the needs of your pupils.

Getting started

It's easy to run the software. Simply insert the CD-ROM into your CD drive and the disk should autorun and launch the interface in your web browser.

If the disk does not autorun, open 'My Computer' and select the CD drive, then open the file 'start.html'.

Please note: this CD-ROM is designed for use on a PC. It will also run on most Apple Macintosh computers in Safari however, due to the differences between Mac and PC fonts, you may experience some unavoidable variations in the typography and page layouts of the activity sheets.

The Menu screen

Four options are available to you from the main menu screen.

The first option takes you to the Activity Sheets screen, where you can choose an activity sheet to edit or print out using Microsoft Word.

(If you do not have the Microsoft Office suite, you might like to consider using OpenOffice instead. This is a multi-platform and multi-lingual office suite, and an 'open-source' project. It is compatible with all other major office suites, and the product is free to download, use and distribute. The homepage for OpenOffice on the Internet is: www.openoffice.org.)

The second option on the main menu screen opens a PDF file of the entire book using Adobe Reader (see below). This format is ideal for printing out copies of the activity sheets or for displaying them, for example on an interactive whiteboard.

The third option allows you to choose a page to edit from a text-only list of the activity sheets, as an alternative to the graphical interface on the Activity Sheets screen.

Adobe Reader is free to download and to use. If it is not already installed on your computer, the fourth link takes you to the download page on the Adobe website.

You can also navigate directly to any of the three screens at any time by using the tabs at the top.

The Activity Sheets screen

This screen shows thumbnails of all the activity sheets in the book. Rolling the mouse over a thumbnail highlights the page number and also brings up a preview image of the page.

Click on the thumbnail to open a version of the page in Microsoft Word (or an equivalent software program, see above.) The full range of editing tools are available to you here to customise the page to suit the needs of your particular pupils. You can print out copies of the page or save a copy of your edited version onto your computer.

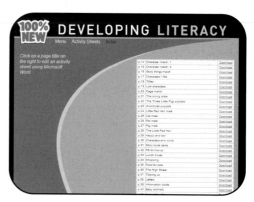

The Index screen

This is a text-only version of the Activity Sheets screen described above. Choose an activity sheet and click on the 'download' link to open a version of the page in Microsoft Word to edit or print out.

Technical support

If you have any questions regarding the *100% New Developing Literacy* or *Developing Mathematics* software, please email us at the address below. We will get back to you as quickly as possible.

educationalsales@acblack.com

Sorting settings

- **Find the stories with the same** settings **.**
- **Put them into groups.**

Tom's Bad Day

2 + 2   7 + 4
3 + 7   6 + 7

The Fairies in the Garden

Ella Gets Lost

The Magic Cake

£1.00

I can do it!

Flowerpot House

Grandad's Garden

The Sand Tray

The Egg

½ Price Eggs

NOW TRY THIS!

- **Look at three books you know.**
- **Tell a friend about the settings.**

Teachers' note Show the children a storybook they know well and ask them where the story took place. Introduce the term *setting* for this and ask them to name or describe the main settings of other stories they know. You could give the children headings into which to sort the storybook cards (home, school, garden or supermarket) or let them do this.

100% New Developing Literacy
Understanding and Responding
to Texts: Ages 5–6
© A & C BLACK

Lost on the beach

- **Put the story in** order .
- Act **the story with a friend.**

Gran came to find Jan.
She gave her a big hug.

Gran lay on a mat.
Jan made sandcastles.

Jan went to find shells.
She got lost.

One sunny day Gran
took Jan to the beach.

NOW TRY THIS!

- **Tell a friend about your day on the beach.**

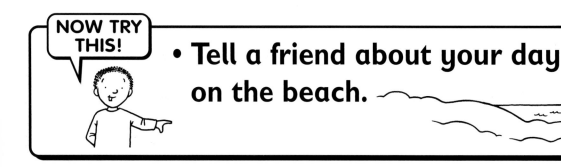

Teachers' note Ask the children to look at the pictures and to decide what is the setting of this story. In pairs, they could read the words beneath the pictures and look for the start of the story. Ask them to cut out the 'pages' and put them in order.

100% New Developing Literacy
Understanding and Responding
to Texts: Ages 5–6
© A & C BLACK

Jan and Gran

- **What do you know about the** | characters | **?**
- **Read the sentences. Tick the right boxes.** ✔

This is Jan. ☐ Gran. ☐

She is a woman. ☐

a girl. ☐

She has long hair. ☐

short hair. ☐

She likes lying in the sunshine. ☐

making sandcastles. ☐

This is Jan. ☐ Gran. ☐

She is a woman. ☐

a girl. ☐

She has long hair. ☐

short hair. ☐

She likes lying in the sunshine. ☐

making sandcastles. ☐

NOW TRY THIS!

- **Write another sentence about Jan.**
- **Write another sentence about Gran.**

Teachers' note Use this with page 14. Ask the children whom the story *Lost on the Beach* was about and introduce the term *character*. Ask them to name the characters and invite them to describe one of them. They can then fill in the character profiles on this page.

100% New Developing Literacy
Understanding and Responding
to Texts: Ages 5–6
© A & C BLACK

What Ali can do

• **Read about Ali.**

Ali can't do up a zip.

He can do up buttons.

He can't do a jigsaw.

He can build a tower.

He can't paint a horse.

He can paint a cat.

He can't ride a bike.

He can skate.

NOW TRY THIS!

• **What can you do?**
• **What can't you do?**
• **Draw and write about these.**

Teachers' note Use this with page 17. It could be presented as a shared or individual activity. Ask the children to read the page and then invite volunteers to name something Ali can or cannot do. You could write up *Can* and *Can't* as headings under which to list these.

100% New Developing Literacy
Understanding and Responding
to Texts: Ages 5–6
© A & C BLACK

What can Ali do?

• **Write on the** lists .

Ali can

_____

_____

_____

_____

Ali can't

_____

_____

_____

_____

 do up a zip

 do up buttons

do a jigsaw

 build a tower

 paint a horse

 paint a cat

 ride a bike

 skate

NOW TRY THIS!

• **Write lists of what another story character can do.**

Teachers' note The children should first have read page 16, which they could use for reference or they could work from memory. Ask them to look at the pictures and read the captions. They can then complete the lists of what Ali can and cannot do.

100% New Developing Literacy
Understanding and Responding
to Texts: Ages 5–6
© A & C BLACK

Brer Rabbit and the Tar Baby

- **Read the story.**
- **What do you think happened next?**

Brer Fox made
a tar baby.

He put the tar baby
on the road. Then he hid.

Hello!

Soon Brer Rabbit
came along.

I'll make you
say hello.

Brer Rabbit hit the
tar baby. His hand stuck.

Let go of
my hand.

He hit the tar baby with
his other hand. It stuck.

Let go of
my hands.

Brer Rabbit kicked the
tar baby. His foot stuck.

NOW TRY THIS!

- **Draw three more pictures.**
- **Write the words.**

Teachers' note This could be presented as a shared or individual activity. The children could take turns to read a sentence, then they can discuss what they think might happen next. Ask them what Brer Rabbit might do and what Brer Fox might do.

100% New Developing Literacy
Understanding and Responding
to Texts: Ages 5–6
© A & C BLACK

• Act the story with a friend.

Please give me some money.

Here are a hundred rupees.

I cannot take it. You did not earn it.

I have never worked. I shall go out and work.

Please give me some work.

You can help me to dig this road.

I can do no more work.

I can pay one rupee.

NOW TRY THIS!

• **How does the king feel?**
• **Tell a friend.**

Teachers' note Read the story with the class and discuss the setting (India long ago) and characters (a Brahmin and a king). Explain that a Brahmin is a priest. You could also talk about the difference between earning money and being given it. The story is continued on page 20.

100% New Developing Literacy Understanding and Responding to Texts: Ages 5–6 © A & C BLACK

- Act the story with a friend.

NOW TRY THIS!

- **How does the king feel now?**
- **Tell a friend.**

Teachers' note Continued from page 19. Continue reading the story with the children and ask them why the Brahmin wanted to talk to the king. Point out that if he had taken the money the king was going to give him at first he would have had a lot more. Ask them if they think he was right not to take it and ask them which money was the more valuable, and why.

100% New Developing Literacy
Understanding and Responding
to Texts: Ages 5–6
© A & C BLACK

Chicken Licken

• **Write what they said.**

The sky is falling down. I'm off to tell the king.

Chicken Licken

Then I shall come too.

Henny Penny

The sky is falling down.
We're off to tell the _____ .

Chicken Licken   Henny Penny

Then _____
_____ .

Cocky Locky

The sky _____
_____
_____ .

_____
_____ .

Chicken Licken
Henny Penny

Cocky Locky

Ducky Lucky

NOW TRY THIS!

Draw the pictures.

• **Soon they met Drakey Lakey.**
• **Write what they said.**
• **Write what Drakey Lakey said.**

Teachers' note The children first need to have read the story *Chicken Licken*. Ask them what Chicken Licken said when the acorn fell on his head. Whom was he going to tell? Which characters does the first picture show and what did Chicken Licken say and what did Henny Penny reply? Repeat this for the other characters.

100% New Developing Literacy
Understanding and Responding
to Texts: Ages 5–6
© A & C BLACK

Henny Penny

Chicken Licken

Cocky Locky

Teachers' note The children should first have completed page 21. Make two character puppets as described on page 6. The children should read the name of their puppet characters and then cut them out. Provide a flat stick (for example, a lollipop stick) for them to glue each one onto. They can then enact the story in their group. See pages 23–24 for more puppets.

**100% New Developing Literacy
Understanding and Responding
to Texts: Ages 5–6**
© A & C BLACK

Drakey Lakey

Ducky Lucky

Turkey Lurkey

Teachers' note The children should first have completed page 21. Make two character puppets as described on page 6 so that each child in a group of four has two character puppets. Ask the children to read the name of their puppet characters and then to cut them out. They can then enact the story in their group. See pages 22 and 24 for more puppets.

100% New Developing Literacy
Understanding and Responding
to Texts: Ages 5–6
© A & C BLACK

23

Goosey Loosey

Foxey Loxey

Teachers' note The children should first have completed page 21. Make two character puppets as described on page 6 so that each child in a group of four has two character puppets. Ask the children to read the name of their puppet characters and then to cut them out. They can then enact the story in their group. See pages 22–23 for more puppets.

**100% New Developing Literacy
Understanding and Responding
to Texts: Ages 5–6**
© A & C BLACK

• **Join the** | questions | **to the** | answers | .

Why did Grandma
have big teeth?

Why did the Gingerbread
Man run away?

Why did Cinderella
run away at midnight?

Why did the Sleeping Beauty
sleep for a hundred years?

The children
wanted to eat him.

A fairy put
a spell on her.

It was really the wolf.

The magic spell
would wear off.

NOW TRY THIS!

• **Why did the Queen tell a man to kill Snow White?**
• **Draw and write about it.**

Teachers' note The children first need to have read, listened to or watched the stories *Little Red Riding Hood*, *The Gingerbread Man*, *Cinderella* and *The Sleeping Beauty*. Ask them why Little Red Riding Hood's grandmother suddenly has big teeth. Show the children how to join the question to the answer by drawing a line. They can then continue to answer the other questions.

100% New Developing Literacy
Understanding and Responding
to Texts: Ages 5–6
© A & C BLACK

Hansel and Gretel trail

Once upon a time		 Woodcutter	 woods

birds

Hansel and Gretel

woods

Wicked Stepmother

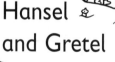
Hansel and Gretel

Witch

They lived happily ever after.	 Woodcutter	 Gretel	 Hansel

NOW TRY THIS!

- **Which part of the story was happy?**
- **Which part was sad?**
- **Tell a friend.**

Teachers' note The children first need to have read, listened to or watched the story *Hansel and Gretel*. They could work in a group. Invite one of them to read the words in the first box. Ask the next child to continue, using the picture as a clue ('Once upon a time there was a little cottage'). The next child uses the next picture to help continue the story, and so on.

100% New Developing Literacy Understanding and Responding to Texts: Ages 5–6
© A & C BLACK

The Princess and the Pea

- **Put the pictures in** order .
- **Tell the story with a friend.**

"Please let me in. I am a princess."

One stormy night a girl came to his castle.

"There is a hard lump in this bed."

The girl could not sleep.

"We'll see if she is a real princess."

The queen put a pea in the bed. Then she put a pile of mattresses on it.

"I cannot find a good princess to marry."

Once upon a time a prince was looking for a princess to marry.

NOW TRY THIS!

- **What happened next?**
- **Tell the rest of the story to a friend.**

Teachers' note You could use this page to introduce the story *The Princess and the Pea* or to help the children to re-tell it. They should first cut out the pictures and put them in order. They can then read the story and predict what happened next.

100% New Developing Literacy Understanding and Responding to Texts: Ages 5–6
© A & C BLACK

Who will help Goldilocks?

- **Goldilocks is lost.**
- **Who will help her?**

The Wolf ☐

Snow White ☐

The Troll ☐

Little Red
Riding Hood ☐

Goldilocks

Hansel and Gretel ☐

The Fairy
Godmother ☐

The Gingerbread Man ☐

The Giant ☐

NOW TRY THIS!

- **How does the character help Goldilocks?**
- **Make up the story with a friend.**

Teachers' note Explain that this activity is about an adventure that Goldilocks had in the woods a few days after she had visited the three bears. Invite volunteers to talk about Goldilocks and each of the other characters depicted, focusing on what the characters were like. Which characters might help Goldilocks, who has lost her way? Some children might be able to make up a story about this.

100% New Developing Literacy
Understanding and Responding
to Texts: Ages 5–6
© A & C BLACK

Fairyland

- **Spot the fairytale** [characters] .
- **Write their names.**

Name-bank

Billy Goat Gruff

Giant

Little Pig

Prince

Sleeping Beauty

Troll

Wolf

NOW TRY THIS!

- **Draw your own fairyland.**
- **Draw three fairytale characters in it.**
- **Write their names.**

Teachers' note Invite volunteers to describe the setting, saying what they can see there. They could identify the characters and say which stories they are from before writing the names of the characters in the label boxes.

100% New Developing Literacy
Understanding and Responding
to Texts: Ages 5–6
© A & C BLACK

The Emerald City

- **Colour the pictures.**
- **Write the missing words.**

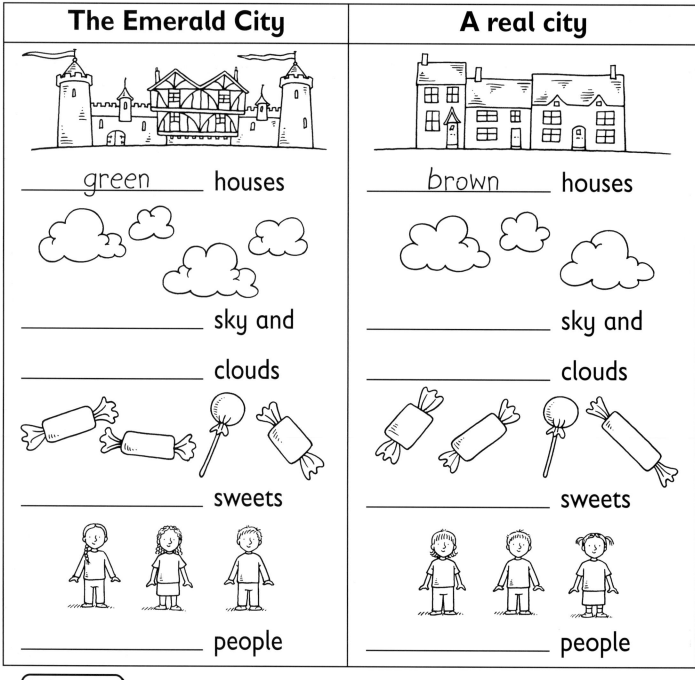

The Emerald City	A real city
green houses	_brown_ houses
_____ sky and	_____ sky and
_____ clouds	_____ clouds
_____ sweets	_____ sweets
_____ people	_____ people

NOW TRY THIS!

- **Draw some drinks from the Emerald City.**
- **Write about them.**

Teachers' note The children first need to have read *The Wizard of Oz*. Ask them where Dorothy set off to along the Yellow Brick Road (the Emerald City) and what it was like there. Remind them of the term *setting* for a place in which a story happens. Discuss how the Emerald City was different from real cities.

100% New Developing Literacy Understanding and Responding to Texts: Ages 5–6
© A & C BLACK

A strange place

- **Draw where you live.**
- **Draw a story** setting .
- **Write** labels .

Think about
homes
cars
plants.

Where I live	Story setting

NOW TRY THIS!

- **How is the story setting different?**
- **Write three sentences about it.**

Teachers' note Ask the children about story settings they know. Focus on those which are set in imaginary worlds (see Introduction, page 5). Ask the children to describe the setting of a story they have been sharing and to say what makes it different from a real place. What is strange about it?

**100% New Developing Literacy
Understanding and Responding
to Texts: Ages 5–6
© A & C BLACK**

What did they want?

• **Write what they said.**

Dorothy

I want to go back

home

The Tin Man

I want a

_____

The Lion

I want a

_____

The Scarecrow

I want to be

_____

NOW TRY THIS!

• **Draw the Wizard of Oz.**
• **Write what he said to Dorothy.**

32

Teachers' note The children first need to have read *The Wizard of Oz*. Ask them to read the names of the characters and to say what they were like. Invite volunteers to say what each character wanted.

100% New Developing Literacy
Understanding and Responding
to Texts: Ages 5–6
© A & C BLACK

Making a salad: lists

- **Each take a list.**
- **Collect the things on the list.**

Four can play.

My salad

carrot

celery

cucumber

red pepper

rocket

My salad

cucumber

lettuce

spring onion

tomato

watercress

My salad

apple

celery

lettuce

spring onion

watercress

My salad

apple

carrot

red pepper

rocket

tomato

Teachers' note Use this with page 34. The children should each have a list and collect the appropriate pictures from page 34. Draw out how a list is useful when they plan what they are going to do and what they need.

100% New Developing Literacy
Understanding and Responding
to Texts: Ages 5–6
© A & C BLACK

Making a salad: ingredients

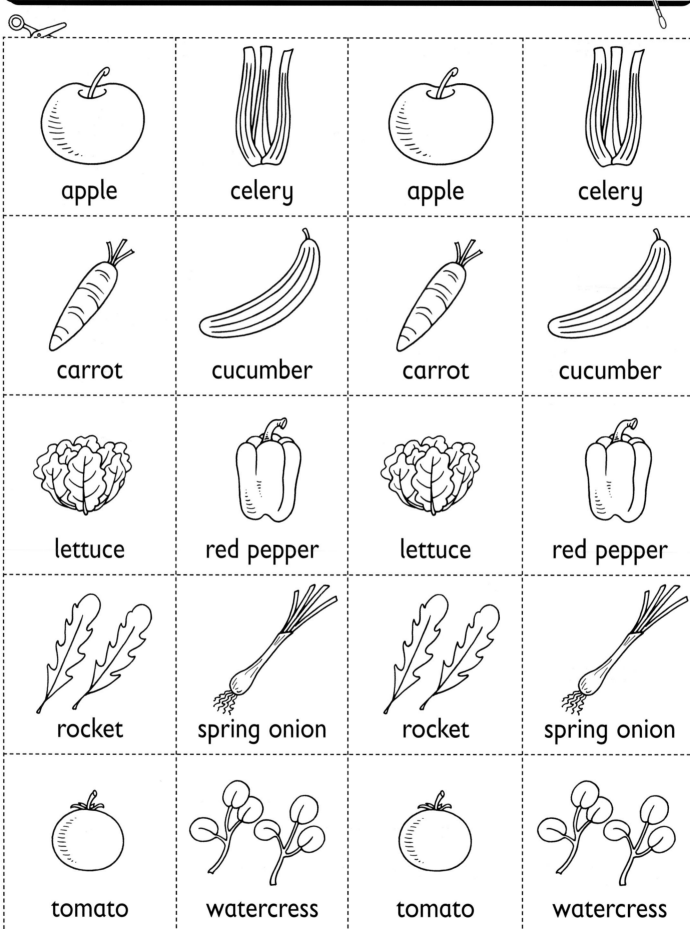

apple	celery	apple	celery
carrot	cucumber	carrot	cucumber
lettuce	red pepper	lettuce	red pepper
rocket	spring onion	rocket	spring onion
tomato	watercress	tomato	watercress

Teachers' note Use this with page 33. The children should each have a list from page 33. They should collect the pictures of the items on their list.

100% New Developing Literacy Understanding and Responding to Texts: Ages 5–6
© A & C BLACK

Victorian seaside search

- **Read the** captions .

A parasol

A bathing machine

A bathing dress

A camera

A donkey

- **Find these.**

Something to ride _____

Something to take pictures _____

Something to wear _____

Something to keep the sun off _____

Something to go into the water _____

_____

NOW TRY THIS!

- **Draw three things you see on a beach.**
- **Write captions for them.**

Teachers' note Present this as a page from an information book. Ask the children to use this page to help them to find the items described.

100% New Developing Literacy Understanding and Responding to Texts: Ages 5–6 © A & C BLACK

Signs

• **Match the** signs **to the pictures.**

Four can play in the house.	Two can paint.
Now wash your hands.	Please put rubbish in here.
Two can play with the puppets.	Three can play in the sand tray.

NOW TRY THIS!

• **Write a sign for somewhere in your school.**

Teachers' note Begin by asking the children to read any signs around the classroom which tell them how to use equipment or materials and how many can use them. Help them to read the signs and then let them match them to the items depicted.

100% New Developing Literacy
Understanding and Responding
to Texts: Ages 5–6
© A & C BLACK

Strawberry milkshake

- **Put the pictures in order.**
- **Put an** ⟦instruction⟧ **with each picture.**
- **Glue them onto paper.**

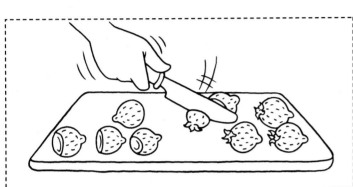

Wash the strawberries.

Wash your hands.

Cut the tops off the strawberries.

Strawberry milkshake
You need:
½ litre milk
8 strawberries
blender
knife
chopping board

NOW TRY THIS!

- **Draw the next picture.**
- **Write the instruction.**

Teachers' note Ask the children to say what each picture tells them to do. In particular, discuss the third picture, which shows all the ingredients needed. The children should cut out the pictures and put them in order, matching the words to the pictures.

100% New Developing Literacy Understanding and Responding to Texts: Ages 5–6
© A & C BLACK

Instructions for robots

- **Read the** instructions .
- **Which robots are right?** ✔
- **Which robots are wrong?** ✘

> Draw a robot with a square head.
>
> Give the robot three eyes.
>
> Make its legs long.
>
> Put wheels under its feet.
>
> Put a screen on its chest.

NOW TRY THIS!

- **Read the instructions again.**
- **Draw another robot.**
- **Use the same instructions.**

Teachers' note Invite volunteers each to read a sentence from the instructions. The children should check each robot to see which ones have been made according to the instructions. If any instruction has not been followed they should put a cross in the box. A tick is only for robots for which all the instructions have been followed.

100% New Developing Literacy
Understanding and Responding
to Texts: Ages 5–6
© A & C BLACK

Instructions machine

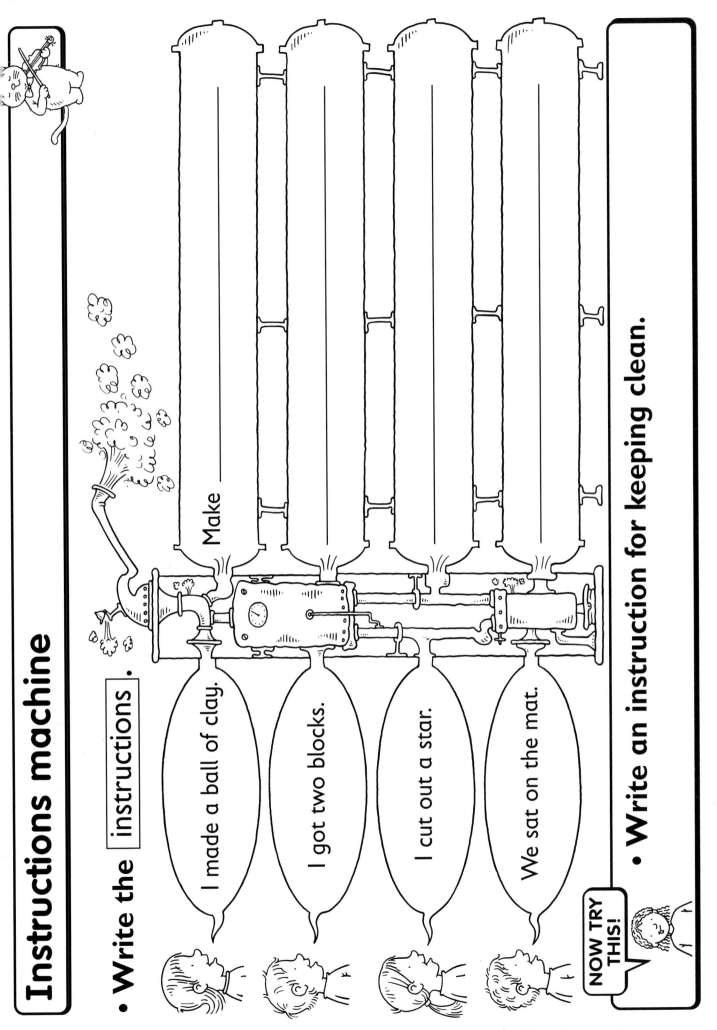

● Write the instructions .

Make

I made a ball of clay.

I got two blocks.

I cut out a star.

We sat on the mat.

● Write an instruction for keeping clean.

NOW TRY THIS!

Teachers' note Tell the children that the instructions machine helps them to turn sentences into instructions. They should read what the children on the page say about what they did and then write these as instructions. You could complete the first one with them as an example.

100% New Developing Literacy
Understanding and Responding
to Texts: Ages 5–6
© A & C BLACK

A day at the farm

- **Put the words and pictures in** order.
- **Read the words.**

At the end of the day we watched the sheepdogs.

First we went to see the cows.

On Monday we went to a farm.

Then we looked at the tractor.

NOW TRY THIS!

- **List the animals on the farm.**

Teachers' note Tell the children that this page is about a class day out at the farm. They wrote it when they got back from their visit but the pictures and writing got mixed up. Ask them to cut them out and put them in order then read the recount to check that it is correct. You could introduce the term *recount* if appropriate.

100% New Developing Literacy
Understanding and Responding
to Texts: Ages 5–6
© A & C BLACK

Questions about the farm

- **Match the** | answers | **to the** | questions |.

Where did the children go?	 Monday
What day was it?	 The cows
Which animals did they see first?	 The tractor
What did they look at next?	 Sheepdogs
Which animals did they watch last?	A farm

NOW TRY THIS!

- **Tell a friend about your day out.**

Teachers' note The children should first have completed page 40. They could refer to that page to help them to answer the questions (by drawing a line from question to answer).

100% New Developing Literacy
Understanding and Responding
to Texts: Ages 5–6
© A & C BLACK

Making things

- **What did they make?**
- **Read the words.**

Ellie made a plane.

May made a flower.

Raj made a car.

Ben made a house.

Jack made a crown.

Leah made a kite.

- **Join the children to what they made.**

Ellie		Ben
May		Jack
Raj		Leah

kite

crown

flower

car

plane

house

NOW TRY THIS!

- **What have you made?**
- **Write a sentence.**

Teachers' note Invite volunteers to read what the children on this page made. The children can then draw lines to link them to the words for the things they made.

100% New Developing Literacy Understanding and Responding to Texts: Ages 5–6 © A & C BLACK

Bed-time

• **Write the sentences in the correct order.**

  I got into bed.

  I put on my pyjamas.

  I got undressed.

  I had a bath.

_____

_____

_____

_____

NOW TRY THIS!

• **Write the next sentence.**

_____

Teachers' note The children could read these sentences as a shared group reading activity and then decide in what order they should be written to make sense as a recount. They should copy them in the correct order.

100% New Developing Literacy
Understanding and Responding
to Texts: Ages 5–6
© A & C BLACK

Picture dictionary: 1

- ## Write the first letters.
- ## Read the words.

__xe	__ell	__ar
__oll	__gg	__lag
__oal	__and	__ce
__umper	__itten	__amp

NOW TRY THIS!

- ## Put these in alphabetical order.

cat   jet   boy   hat

Teachers' note These are pages from a picture dictionary, in alphabetical order. You might need to remind the children what this means and display an alphabet strip. They can then write the missing initial letter of each word. Ask them to read the words with a friend. When they have completed the page, ask them which letter comes next.

**100% New Developing Literacy
Understanding and Responding
to Texts: Ages 5–6**
© A & C BLACK

- **Write the first letters.**
- **Read the words.**

__ op	__ ine	__ range
__ an	__ ueen	__ ose
__ un	__ ractor	__ nicorn
__ an	__ heel	__ -ray

NOW TRY THIS!

- **Draw things that begin with** y **and** z **.**
- **Write the words.**

Use a dictionary.

Teachers' note The children should first have completed page 44. You might need to remind them what a picture dictionary is and display an alphabet strip. They can then write the missing initial letter of each word. Ask them to read the words with a friend. When they have completed the page, ask them which letter comes next.

100% New Developing Literacy
Understanding and Responding
to Texts: Ages 5–6
© A & C BLACK

Page by page

- **Put the fruits on their dictionary pages.**
- **Write the words.**

elderberries   banana   fig

kiwi   damson   lychee

mango   grapes   apple

a	b	cd
_____	_____	_____

e	f	ghi
_____	_____	_____

jk	l	mn
_____	_____	_____

NOW TRY THIS!

- **Write a fruit on each page.**

no	pqr	st
_____	_____	_____

Teachers' note Tell the children that the boxes with letters in them are dictionary pages and help them to read the captions of the pictures of fruit. They should then write these words on the correct 'pages'.

100% New Developing Literacy
Understanding and Responding
to Texts: Ages 5–6
© A & C BLACK

All in order

• **List each group in** alphabetical order .

Beth Alan Clare

_____
_____
_____

Fiona Dan Emma

_____
_____
_____

Imran Harry Gina

_____
_____
_____

Leo Jan Karl

_____
_____
_____

NOW TRY THIS!

• **Write four of your friends' names.**
• **List them in alphabetical order.**

Choose names that begin with different letters.

Teachers' note Remind the children what is meant by alphabetical order and help them to identify the first name, alphabetically in the first group. (Children could start by circling the first letter of each name.) Ask them which name comes next and which comes third. They should then list the names alphabetically and repeat this for each group.

100% New Developing Literacy Understanding and Responding to Texts: Ages 5–6
© A & C BLACK

Titles game

- **Two can play.**
- **Collect** fiction **or** non-fiction.
- **Put the cards face down.**
- **Take turns to pick up a card.**

Keep only the cards for your set.

All About Ants 	Jack and the Beanstalk 	 Cinderella
India 	Homes  Long Ago	 Goldilocks and the Three Bears
My Learn to Cook Book 	 Little Red Riding Hood	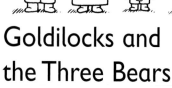 Farm Animals
 Dogs	Elmer 	The Very Hungry  Caterpillar

Teachers' note Cut out the cards and turn them face down. The children play in pairs – each collects either fiction or non-fiction. They take turns to pick up a card, which they keep if it is of the type they are collecting, and have another try. If not, they replace it face down and it is the other child's turn.

100% New Developing Literacy Understanding and Responding to Texts: Ages 5–6 © A & C BLACK

Book choice

- ## Which books might help?
- ## Draw a line to join each child to a book.

Where do lions come from?

What is a newt?

What is it like on Mars?

Florence Nightingale

The Big Cats

Ladybirds

The Planets

Picture A B C Dictionary

Victorian Homes

How did the Victorians clean their homes?

How many legs does a ladybird have?

What did Florence Nightingale do?

NOW TRY THIS!

- ## Find a book to answer this question.
  How are bricks made?

Look in your class library.

Teachers' note Show the children some information books and point out that they are non-fiction books because they give information and do not tell stories. Hold up each one and ask, 'Will this book help me to find out about ... (for example, the moon, flowers, rivers)?' The children can then decide which book will help each of these children and draw lines linking them to the books.

100% New Developing Literacy Understanding and Responding to Texts: Ages 5–6
© A & C BLACK

What we know

- Work with a friend.
- Write what you know about metal things.

Metal things

Write in the boxes.

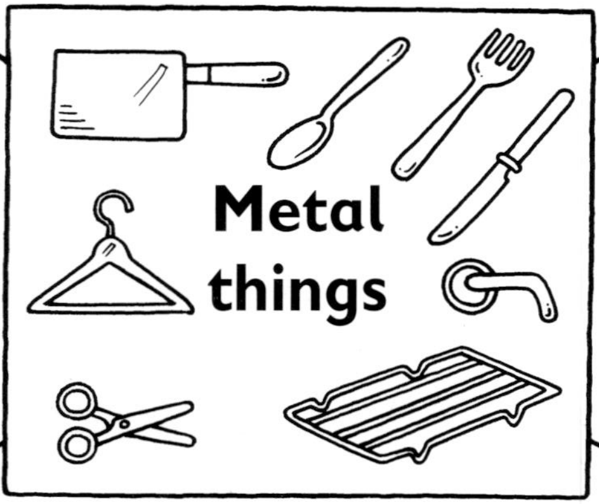

NOW TRY THIS!

- Write what you want to know about metal things.

Teachers' note This could be used in connection with work in science on materials. You could begin by letting the children examine some metal things. The children should make simple notes about what they know, in the form of lists. Model how to complete one of the boxes: for example, list some items made of metal.

100% New Developing Literacy
Understanding and Responding
to Texts: Ages 5–6
© A & C BLACK

A closer look

- **Read the questions about homes in the past.**
- **Find a book to help.**

How did they do the washing? ☐

What were the floors like? ☐

What were the cookers like? ☐

How did they keep the house warm? ☐

- **Which book will help?**
- **Write the title.**

- **Which questions can you answer?** ✔

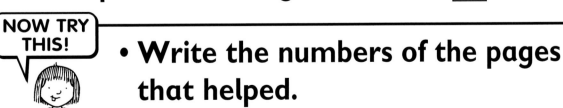

NOW TRY THIS!

- **Write the numbers of the pages that helped.**

Teachers' note Ask the children to look for a book which might help. They should copy the title of the book and look through it to find the answer to one of the questions. They tick that question. During the plenary session, invite volunteers to read the question and to give an answer that they have found in a book. Discuss how they found this answer.

100% New Developing Literacy Understanding and Responding to Texts: Ages 5–6 © A & C BLACK

Finding out

- **You need a question-and-answer book.**
- **Write** yes **or** no .

 Are a leopard's spots brown? _____

 Do snakes lay eggs? _____

 Matzah Is Passover a Hindu festival? _____

 Is a sponge an animal? _____

 Is the moon yellow? _____

 Do stars have five points? _____

NOW TRY THIS!

- **Write another question.**
- **Find the answer in a book.**

Teachers' note Ensure that the children have access to a book about plants. Ask them to read the questions (with a friend, if necessary), and to make up three questions of their own about plants. During the plenary session, ask the children to say their questions and to demonstrate how they found the answers.

100% New Developing Literacy Understanding and Responding to Texts: Ages 5–6 © A & C BLACK

Rain

- **Read the poem.**
- **Do the actions.**

Rain on the grass,

Rain on the tree,

Rain on the roof-top,

But not on me.

NOW TRY THIS!

- **Learn the poem.**
- **Say the poem and do the actions.**

Don't look at the page!

Teachers' note The children could read the poem as a group or individually – first without the actions and then with them. Help them to learn it a line at a time so that they can recite it. They could also adjust this for light rain for the first picture, heavier rain for the second, and then for a downpour.

100% New Developing Literacy
Understanding and Responding
to Texts: Ages 5–6
© A & C BLACK

Mud

- **You need a tray of sloppy wet sand.**

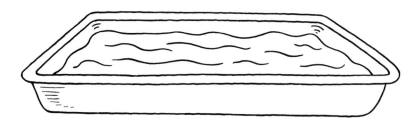

- **Slop the sand and read the poem.**

I like mud.
The slippy, sloppy, squelchy kind.

The slap it into pies kind.

Stir it up in puddles,
Slither and slide,

I do like mud.

by Shirley Hughes

NOW TRY THIS!

- **Circle the** s **sounds.**
- **These make the sloppy sound.**

Teachers' note Provide a tray of very wet sand to represent mud and let the children handle it as you read the poem. Encourage the children to join in the poem as they slop the sand about. Talk about other 'sloppy' materials and even, during another lesson, make some of them: for example, a mixture of cornflour and water, coloured with food dye.

100% New Developing Literacy
Understanding and Responding
to Texts: Ages 5–6
© A & C BLACK

Treasure hunt

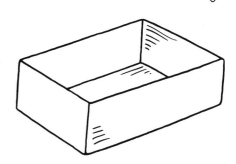

- **You need a plastic tray or box.**
- **Read the words.**
- **Collect things like that.**
- **Tick each one you collect.**

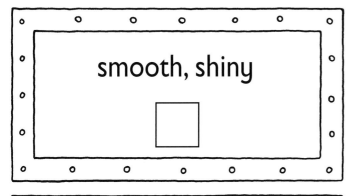

smooth, shiny

crispy, crackly

slippy, sloppy

cold, crunchy

wet, wiggly

dry, dusty

NOW TRY THIS!

- **Collect two more things.**
- **Write words for them.**

Teachers' note Ensure that each child has a plastic tray or small box for collecting. They should read the words and look for an item to match each description. Discuss why they should not pick up any animals or other creatures. During the plenary session you could read the descriptions aloud and invite volunteers to display the appropriate objects.

100% New Developing Literacy Understanding and Responding to Texts: Ages 5–6 © A & C BLACK

Loud and quiet

- **Which words are** loud ?
- **Which words are** quiet ?
- **Read the words.**
- **Write** loud **or** quiet .

Susie sleeping softly.

Bob bashing bricks.

Peter peeling potatoes.

Jasmin jumping for joy.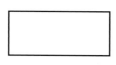

Carla crashing cars.

NOW TRY THIS!

- **Write something** loud .
- **Write something** quiet .

Teachers' note Read the first example with the children and ask them if the words should be read quietly or loudly. Let them try both to find out. They can then write *loud* or *quiet* in the box. Ask them to read the other examples and to decide whether they are loud or quiet.

100% New Developing Literacy Understanding and Responding to Texts: Ages 5–6 © A & C BLACK

I threw a pie

• **Fill in the gaps with** rhyming **words.**

I threw a pie up in the _____.

I threw a chair up in the _____.

I threw a ball over the _____.

I threw a door down on the _____.

I threw a mop into the _____.

• **Write rhymes about throwing these.**

a car   a pin   some meat

Teachers' note Read the first example and invite the children to supply a rhyming word. Remind them of their previous learning about rhyme. Emphasise that the actions should be pretended, not real, before the children read the examples, do the actions and write the missing words.

100% New Developing Literacy Understanding and Responding to Texts: Ages 5–6
© A & C BLACK

I spy characters

- **Match these to the** I spy **cards.**
- **Write their names on the cards.**

three blind mice

Little Boy Blue

Jack Sprat

a cat with a fiddle

Mary Mary

Margery Daw

Little Bo Peep

Jack and Jill

NOW TRY THIS!

- **Write an** I spy **rhyme for Old King Cole.**

Teachers' note Use the characters with the 'I spy' cards from page 59 in different ways. The simplest is to give each child a copy of this page and explain that the nursery rhyme characters are hiding in unexpected places. Place the 'I spy' cards face down and let the children take turns to pick one up. They read it aloud and the first to say which character it describes keeps it.

100% New Developing Literacy Understanding and Responding to Texts: Ages 5–6
© A & C BLACK

I spy cards

Look in the car,
Look in the jeep,
I spy
_____

Look in a slipper,
Look in a shoe,
I spy
_____

Look in the kitchen,
Look in the dairy,
I spy
_____

Look under the carpet,
Look under the mat,
I spy
_____

Look in the farm,
Look in the mill,
I spy
_____

Look in the snow,
Look in the ice,
I spy
_____

Look on the ceiling,
Look on the floor,
I spy
_____

Look on the top,
Look on the middle,
I spy
_____

NOW TRY THIS!

• **Finish the rhyme.**

Look down the road,
Look round the corner,
I spy
_____

Teachers' note Use this with page 58. One way to copy the character cards onto different colours and place them in two sets face down. Explain that the characters are hiding in unexpected places. The children take turns to pick up a card from each set, and decide whether they match. If so, they keep them and, if not, they place them face back down. The child with the most pairs wins.

100% New Developing Literacy
Understanding and Responding
to Texts: Ages 5–6
© A & C BLACK

Skipping rhyme

• **Match the places to the** skipping rhyme .

Up and down,
Up and down,
All the way to____

Downing Street

Butcher's Shop
3
Meats

Out and in,
Out and in,
All the way to____

Heel and toe,
Heel and toe,
All the way to____

London Town

King's Lynn

Hands and feet,
Hands and feet,
All the way to____

Skip and hop,
Skip and hop,
All the way to____

Battersea

Pimlico

Elbow, knee,
Elbow, knee,
All the way to____

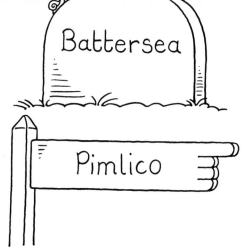

NOW TRY THIS!

• **Learn one rhyme.**
• **Say it when you skip.**

Try making up more verses.

Teachers' note Begin by reading the words on the signs with the children. Explain that these are the names of places and ask if they know any of them. Introduce the rhyme by chanting the first verse while skipping (or ask an older child to do this). Emphasise the skipping rhythm. Stop at the missing word and ask the children to supply it.

100% New Developing Literacy
Understanding and Responding
to Texts: Ages 5–6
© A & C BLACK

Lines

- **Read the poems aloud.**
- **Write them on the** lines **.**

One, two, three, four, Mary at the cottage door, Eating cherries off a plate, Five, six, seven, eight.

_____

_____

_____

_____

Man fat, Top hat, Fell flat, Squashed hat.

_____

_____

_____

_____

NOW TRY THIS!

- **Copy another poem in a long line.**
- **Give it to a friend to split into lines.**

Teachers' note Read the first example with the children and ask them if it looks like a poem. Show them another poem and discuss the differences in the way they look. Draw out that a poem is usually set out in separate lines. Help the children to identify the ends of lines and the beginnings of the next ones, also pointing out the capital letters.

100% New Developing Literacy Understanding and Responding to Texts: Ages 5–6 © A & C BLACK

Bubbling porridge

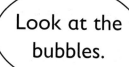

- **Read the** poem.
- **Find the missing words.**
- **Write them in the gaps.**

Look at the bubbles.

plop

bubbling

hot

eat

pot

Porridge is _____

Bubbling hot

Stir it round

In the _____

The bubbles plip

The bubbles _____

It's ready to _____

All bubbling _____

Anon.

NOW TRY THIS!

- **Read the poem with a friend.**
- **One of you reads.**
- **The other makes bubbling sounds.**

Teachers' note Read this in connection with poems about food. If possible, make some porridge and let the children listen to it bubbling in the pan, talking about the sounds it makes. They could read the poem aloud to help them to identify the missing words; encourage them to memorise it.

100% New Developing Literacy Understanding and Responding to Texts: Ages 5–6 © A & C BLACK

Picture this: seaside poems

- **Read a** seaside **poem.**
- **Choose the best picture for it.**

Seaside

Sand in the sandwiches,
Sand in the tea,
Flat, wet sand running
Down to the sea.
Pools full of seaweed,
Shells and stones,
Damp bathing suits
And ice cream cones.

Shirley Hughes

Until I Saw the Sea

Until I saw the sea
I did not know
that wind
could wrinkle water so.

I never knew
that sun
could splinter a whole sea of blue.

Nor
did I know before,
a sea breathes in and out
upon a shore.

Lilian Moore

At the Seaside

When I was down by the sea
A wooden spade they gave to me
To dig the sandy shore.
My holes were empty like a cup,
In every hole the sea came up
Till it could come up no more.

Robert Louis Stevenson

I Saw a Ship

I saw a ship a-sailing
A-sailing on the sea;
And, oh! It was all laden
With pretty things for me!

There were comfits in the cabin
And apples in the hold;
The sails were made of silk,
And the masts were made of gold.

The four-and-twenty sailors
That stood upon the decks,
Were four-and-twenty white mice
With chains about their necks.

The captain was a duck;
With a packet on his back;
And when the ship began to move,
The captain said, "Quack! Quack!"

Anon

Teachers' note Use this with page 64. Read the poems as a shared reading activity (possibly over the course of several short lessons). The children can then cut them out to match with the pictures on page 64 and glue them onto paper or into a personal poetry anthology.

**100% New Developing Literacy
Understanding and Responding
to Texts: Ages 5–6
© A & C BLACK**

Picture this: seaside pictures

- **Choose the best picture for your** [seaside] **poem.**
- **Tell a partner why you chose it.**
- **Colour the picture to match the poem.**

NOW TRY THIS!

- **Find another seaside poem.**
- **Learn the poem.**
- **Draw a picture for it.**

Look in poetry books.

Teachers' note Use this with page 63. After reading the poems with the children and discussing the pictures they conjure up ask the children to cut them out to match with the pictures on this page. They could glue them into a personal poetry anthology.

100% New Developing Literacy Understanding and Responding to Texts: Ages 5–6
© A & C BLACK